Teddy Horsley Books for Young Christians

75p

The Windy Day

Teddy Horsley celebrates Pentecost on Whit Sunday

G000293299

by Leslie J. Francis and Nicola M. Slee

Pictures by Ferelith Eccles Williams

COLLINS

Collins Liturgical Publications
187 Piccadilly, London W1V 9DA

Collins Liturgical Australia
PO Box 3023 Sydney 2001

ISBN 0 00 599748 8

First published 1983

Made and printed in Glasgow
by William Collins Sons & Co Ltd

It is a windy day,
and Teddy Horsley is a puzzled bear.

He opens his eyes to look for the wind,
and cannot see it.

But he sees the wind shake apples down,

turn washing inside out,

and blow paper along the street.

He stretches out his paws to touch the wind,
and cannot feel it.

But he feels the wind push him along,

tug his kite into the sky,

and drive rain into his face.

He pricks up his ears to listen to the wind,
and cannot hear it.

But he hears the wind rattle dustbin lids,

slam doors shut,

and whistle through the trees.

Teddy Horsley knows that the wind is there,
all around him.

The church is celebrating Pentecost,
and Teddy Horsley is a puzzled bear.

He opens his eyes to look for the Holy Spirit,
and cannot see Him.

But he sees the Holy Spirit making people smile
and dance.

He stretches out his paws to touch the Holy Spirit,
and cannot feel Him.

But he feels the Holy Spirit making him safe and loved.

He pricks up his ears to listen to the Holy Spirit, and cannot hear Him.

But he hears the Holy Spirit making people sing and laugh.

Teddy Horsley knows that the Holy Spirit is there,
all around him.